Colour, play and learn
Spanish
with Mia

This book belongs to

ISBN 978-1-7398933-0-9

A catalogue record for this book is available from the British Library

Contents - Contenido

Colours - Colores

Purple - Morado

Pink - Rosa

Yellow - Amarillo

Red - Rojo

Blue - Azul

Green - Verde

Brown - Marrón

Grey - Gris

Orange - Naranja

Black - Negro

White - Blanco

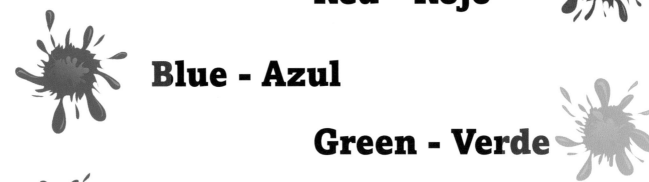

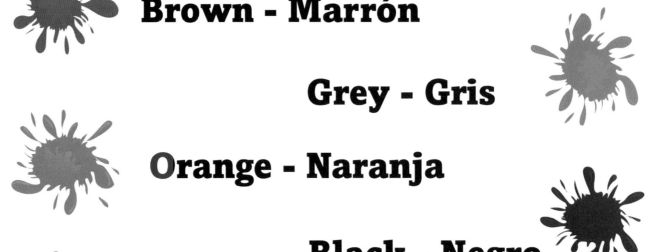

Colours - Colores

Can you colour in Mia?

Orange - Naranja

Purple - Morado

Red - Rojo

Green - Verde

Pink - Rosa

Yellow - Amarillo

Blue - Azul

Colours - Colores

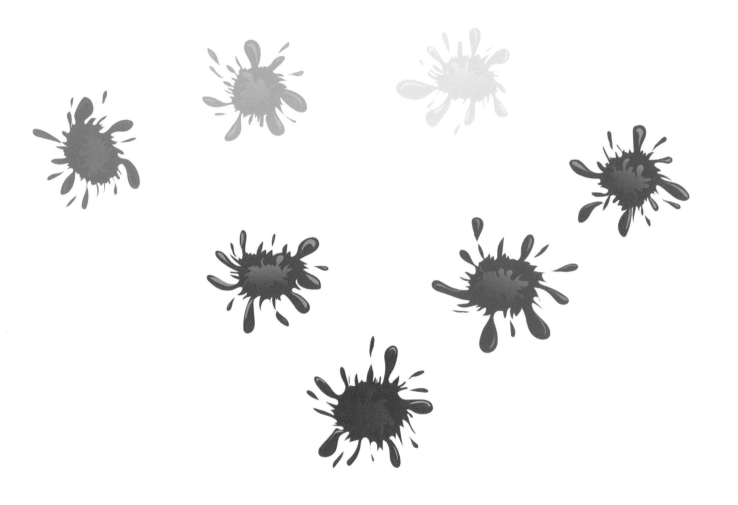

Azul

Verde

Rosa

Morado

Amarillo

Gris

Rojo

Can you match the colours?

Colours - Colores

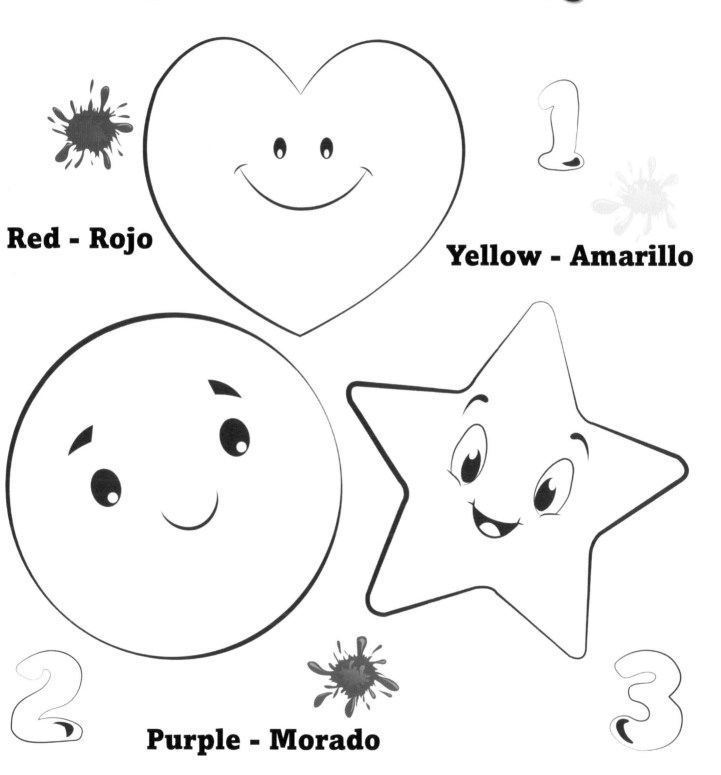

Red - Rojo

Yellow - Amarillo

Purple - Morado

Can you colour in Mia's friends?

Colours - Colores

O	L	L	I	R	A	M	A
V	X	R	Y	N	Q	S	K
E	M	O	R	A	D	O	L
R	W	J	M	B	U	H	U
D	Z	O	R	O	S	A	Z
E	N	A	R	A	N	J	A

Wordsearch – Can you find these words?

Morado

Amarillo

Azul

Rosa

Rojo

Verde

Naranja

Colours - Colores

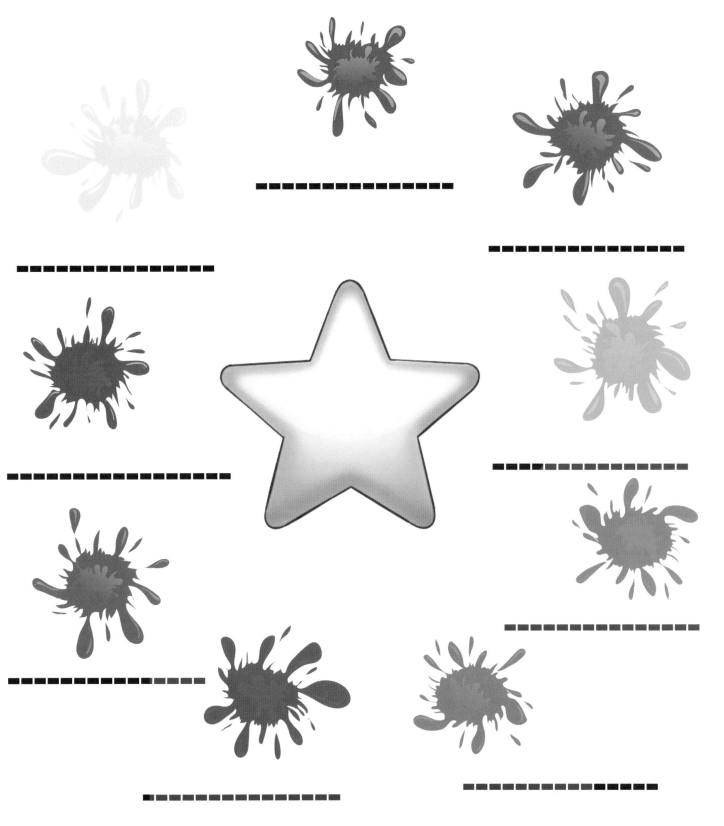

Can you write the colours in Spanish?

Colours - Colores

| | O | R | A | | |

| | | | A |

| A | M | A | | | L | L | |

| | Z | | |

| | | R | | |

| R | | | O |

| | | R | | | J | A |

Can you fill in the gaps?

Numbers - Números

1   **One - uno**

2   **Two - Dos**

3   **Three - Tres**

4   **Four - Cuatro**

5   **Five - Cinco**

6   **Six - Seis**

7   **Seven - Siete**

8   **Eight - Ocho**

9   **Nine - Nueve**

10   **Ten - Diez**

Can you colour in the numbers?

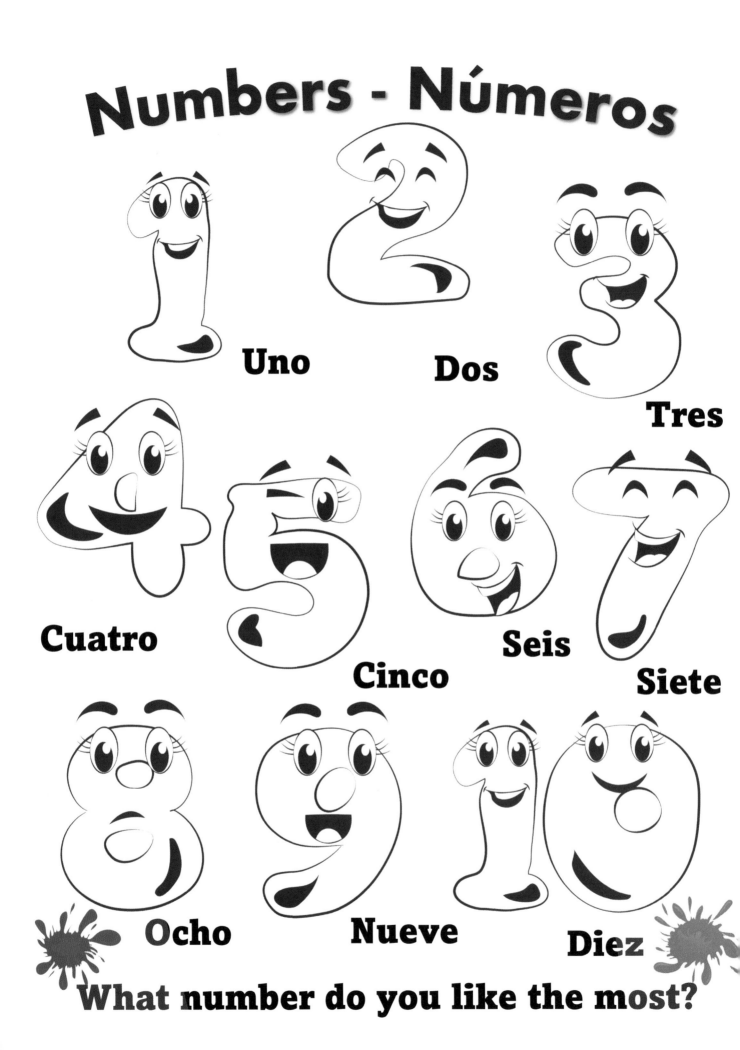

Numbers - Números

  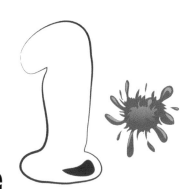

Eight - Ocho

Nine - Nueve

One - uno

Seven - Siete

Two - Dos

Six - Seis

Five - Cinco

Four - Cuatro

Three - Tres

Can you colour in the numbers?

Numbers - Números

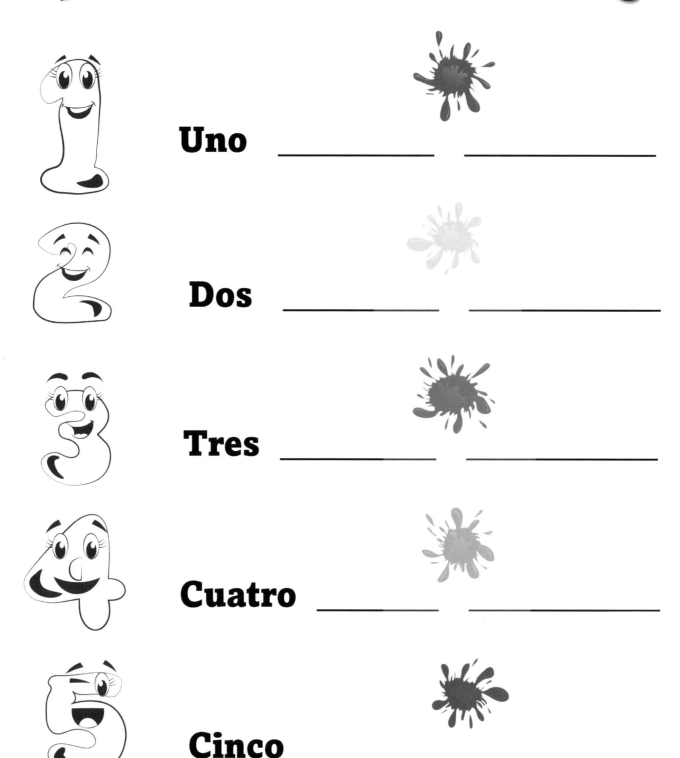

Uno _____ _____

Dos _____ _____

Tres _____ _____

Cuatro _____ _____

Cinco _____ _____

Can you copy the name of the numbers?

Numbers - Números

Ocho

Nueve

Seis

Siete

Can you match the numbers ?

Numbers - Números

N	S	E	R	T	P	X	U
C	U	S	H	D	G	C	N
I	A	E	E	O	C	H	O
N	J	I	V	S	A	Q	LX
C	Z	S	I	E	T	E	I
O	T	O	R	T	A	U	C

Wordsearch - Can you find these words?

 **Uno**   **Cuatro**   **Siete**

 Dos   **Cinco**   **Ocho**

 Tres   **Seis**   **Nueve**

Numbers - Números

Can you write the numbers in Spanish?

Numbers - Números

8 9 1

- -

7 2

- - - - - - - - - - -

6 3

- - - - - - - - - - - - - - - - - - - -

5 4

- -

Can you name and colour in the numbers?

Numbers - Números

Can you draw an " OCHO "?

Colours - Colores
Numbers - Números

Morado

Amarillo

Verde

Rojo

   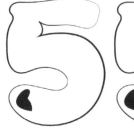

Azul

Can you colour in the numbers?

Colours - Colores
Numbers - Números

Can you solve it?

Pets
Mascotas

..... **Rabbit - Conejo**

..... **Cat - Gato**

..... **Dog - Perro**

..... **Horse - Caballo**

Farm animals
Animales de granja

..... Cow - Vaca

 Hen - Gallina .....

..... Sheep - Oveja

 Pig - Cerdo

Chick - Pollito .....

 ..... Duck - Pato

Wild animals
Animales salvajes

..... **Elephant - Elefante**

..... **Zebra - Cebra**

Giraffe - Jirafa .....

.....
**Hippopotamus -
Hipopótamo**

Lion - León .....

Animals - Animales

Elefante

Jirafa

Conejo

Gato

Caballo

Vaca

Cebra

León

Pato

Oveja

Gallina

Perro

Can you colour in the animals?

Animals - Animales

Perro

Léon

Pato

Vaca

Elefante

Cerdo

Can you match the animals?

Animals - Animales

| J | I | R | | | |

| | | C | |

| | | F | | | | T | E |

| | | | N |

| V | E | | |

| P | | | |

| P | | | | I | T | O |

Can you fill in the gaps?

Animals - Animales

Can you name and colour in the animals?

Animals - Animales

Can you solve it?

Colour in the animal you like the most!

Animals - Animales

Can you draw a " Gato "?

Fruits - Frutas

 ..... **Banana - Plátano**

 ..... **Orange - Naranja**

 ..... **Strawberries - Fresas**

 ..... **Pineapple - Piña**

 ..... **Pear - Pera**

Fruits - Frutas

 ..... **Cherries - Cerezas**

 ..... **Watermelon - Sandia**

 ..... **Lemon - Limón**

 ..... **Grapes - Uvas**

 ..... **Apple - Manzana**

Fruits - Frutas

Can you colour the "plátano"?

Fruits - Frutas

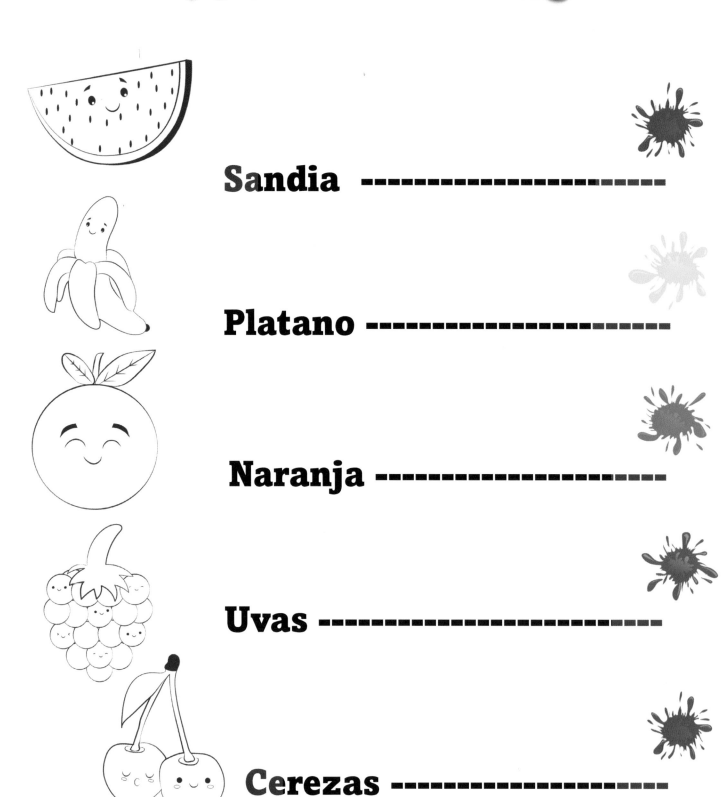

Sandia ----------------------------

Platano ----------------------------

Naranja ----------------------------

Uvas ----------------------------

Cerezas ----------------------------

Can you copy the name of the fruits and colour them in?

Fruits - Frutas

S	A	S	E	R	F	V	S
U	R	N	J	P	B	L	A
D	E	W	H	I	Z	I	N
Y	P	Q	U	Ñ	L	M	D
P	L	A	T	A	N	O	I
F	M	A	N	Z	A	N	A

Wordsearch - Can you find these words?

 **Plátano**

 **Limón**

 Fresas **Sandia** **Pera**

  **Piña** **Manzana**

Fruits - Frutas

Can you name and colour in the fruits?

Fruits - Frutas

Can you draw a " PIÑA "?

Vocabulary - Vocabulario

colours - Colores

Spanish - English		Spanish pronunciation	
Azul	Blue	Azul _____	ah - thool
Rojo	Red	Rojo _____	rroh - hoh
Rosa	Pink	Rosa _____	rroh - sah
Verde	Green	Verde _____	behr - deh
Amarillo	Yellow	Amarillo _____	ah – mah – ree - yoh
Naranja	Orange	Naranja _____	nah - rahng - hah
Morado	Purple	Morado _____	moh - rah – doh
Gris	Grey	Gris _____	grees
Negro	Black	Negro _____	neh - groh
Marrón	Brown	Marrón _____	mah - rronh
Blanco	White	Blanco _____	blahn - koh

Numbers - Números

Uno	One	Uno _____	oo - noh
Dos	Two	Dos _____	dohs
Tres	Three	Tres _____	trehs
Cuatro	Four	Cuatro _____	kwah - troh
Cinco	Five	Cinco _____	thin - koh
Seis	Six	Seis _____	seys
Siete	Seven	Siete _____	see - e - teh
Ocho	Eight	Ocho _____	oh – choh
Nueve	Nine	Nueve _____	noo – eh - veh
Diez	Ten	Diez _____	dee - ehs

Vocabulary - Vocabulario

Animals – Animales

Spanish - English		Spanish pronunciation	
Gato	Cat	Gato _____	gah - toh
Perro	Dog	Perro _____	peh - rroh
Conejo	Rabbit	Conejo _____	koh - neh - hoh
Caballo	Horse	Caballo _____	kah - bah - yoh
Vaca	Cow	Vaca _____	bah - kah
Oveja	Sheep	Oveja _____	o - beh - hah
Cerdo	Pig	Cerdo _____	thehr - doh
Pollito	Chick	Pollito _____	poh - yee - toh
Pato	Duck	Pato _____	pah - toh
Gallina	Hen	Gallina _____	gah - yee - nah
Elefante	Elephant	Elefante _____	eh- leh- fahn- teh
Cebra	Zebra	Cebra _____	theh - brah
Jirafa	Giraffe	Jirafa _____	hee - rah - fah
Hipopótamo	Hippopotamus	Hipopótamo _	ee-poh-poh-tah-moh
León	Lion	León _____	le – on

Fruits - Frutas

Plátano	Banana	Plátano _____	plah – tah - noh
Fresa	Strawberries	Fresa _____	freh - sah
Limón	Lemon	Limón _____	lee - mohn
Naranja	Orange	Naranja _____	nah – rahng - hah
Piña	Pineapple	Piña _____	pee - nyah
Pera	Pear	Pera _____	peh - rah
Cerezas	Cherries	Cerezas _____	theh - reh - thah
Sandia	Watermelon	Sandia _____	sahn - dee - ah
Uvas	Grapes	Uvas _____	oo - bahs
Manzana	Apple	Manzana _____	mahn- thah- nah

Answers - Respuestas

Colores

O	L	L	I	R	A	M	A
V		R					
E	M	O	R	A	D	O	L
R		J					
D		O	R	O	S	A	Z
E	N	A	R	A	N	J	A

(With column: L / U / Z on the right side and VERDE down the left)

Números

N	N	S	E	R	T	
C	U	S		D		
I		E		O	C	H O
N		I	V	S		
C		S	I	E	T E	
O		O	R	T	A U C	

(With U / N / O on the right; CINCO down the left; OCHO)

Frutas

S	A	S	E	R	F	S
	R		P		L	A
	E		I		I	N
	P		Ñ		M	D
P	L	A	T	A N O	I	
	M	A	N	Z A N A		

Answers - Respuestas

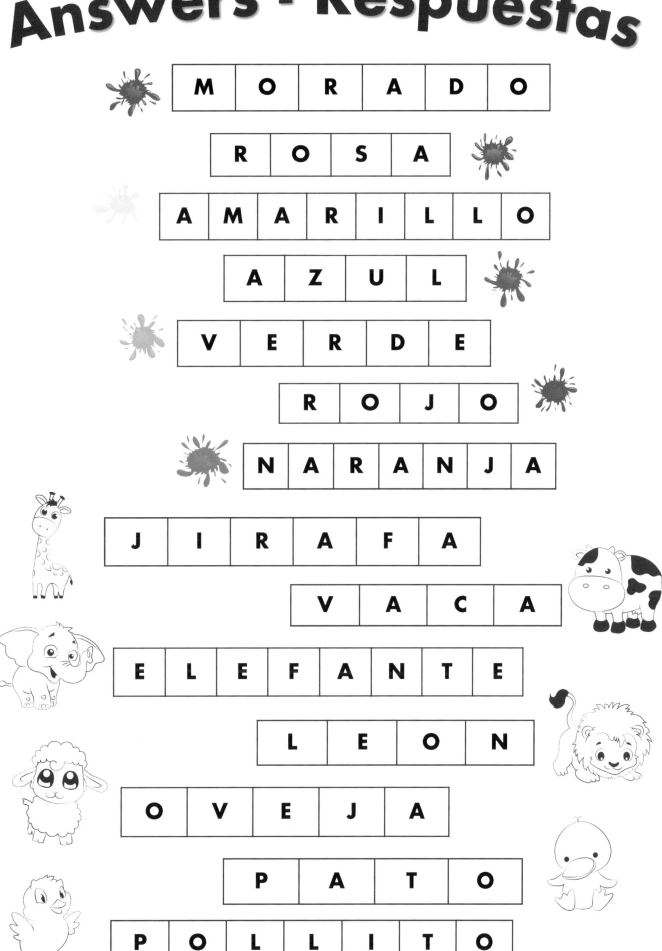

MORADO

ROSA

AMARILLO

AZUL

VERDE

ROJO

NARANJA

JIRAFA

VACA

ELEFANTE

LEON

OVEJA

PATO

POLLITO

Answers - Respuestas

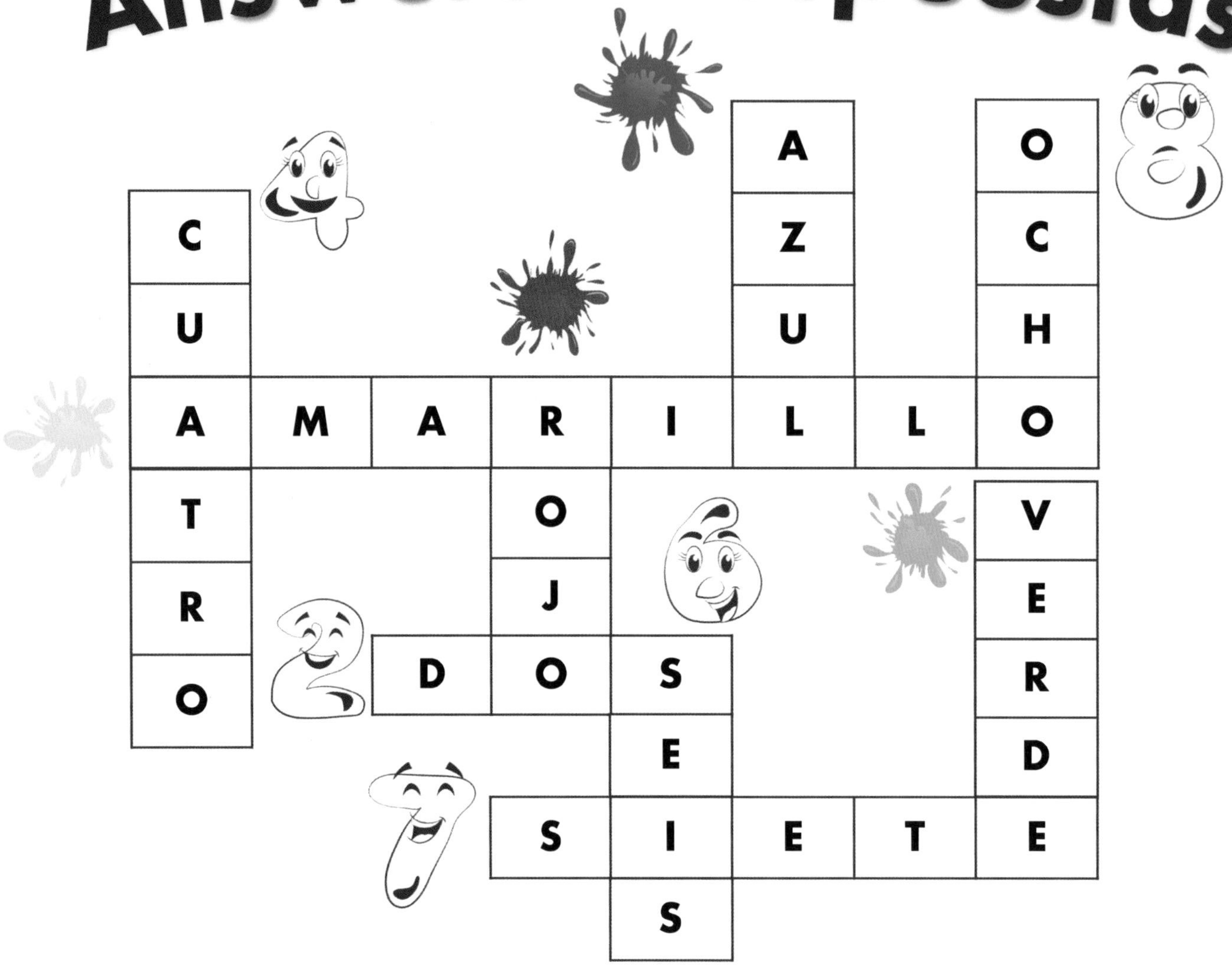
CUATRO
AMARILLO
AZUL
OCHO
ROJO
DOS
SEIS
SIETE
VERDE

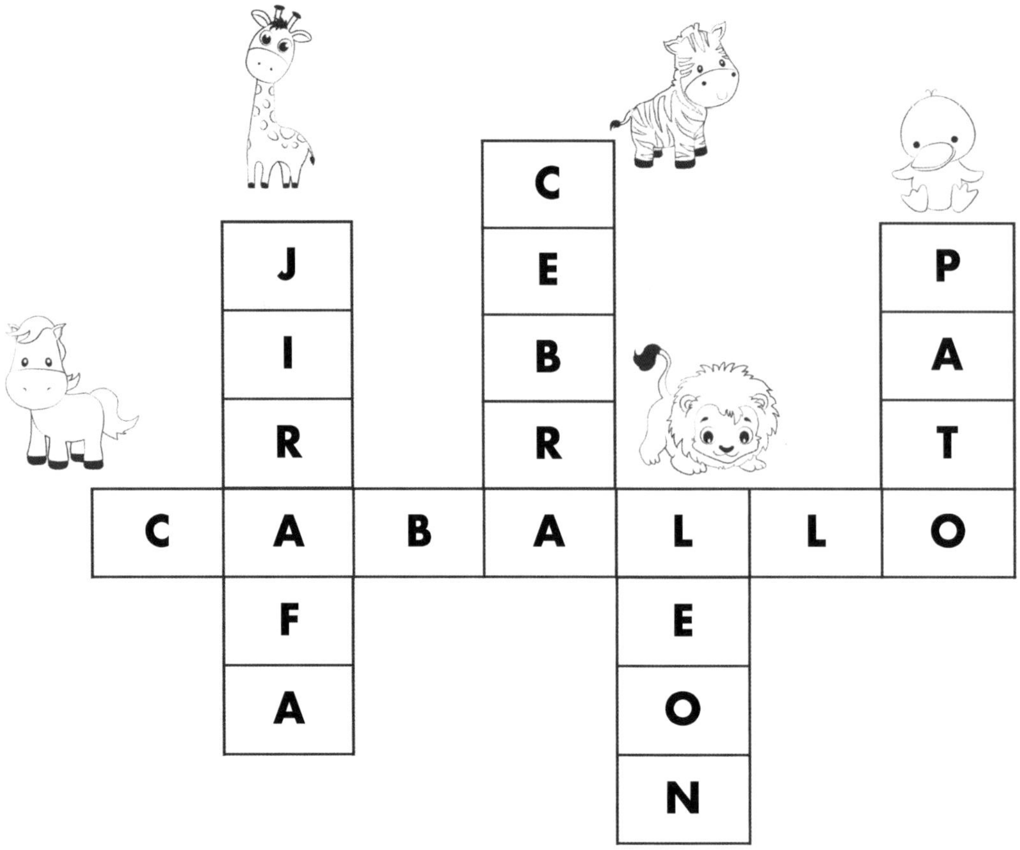
JIRAFA
CEBRA
PATO
CABALLO
LEON

Coming soon

Types of Transport

Clothes

Learn Spanish

Learn German

Household items

Shapes

Learn Italian

Learn French

Alphabet

Body parts

School items

Other titles within this series available. For extra resources, videos and lots more join our community:

www.nereakennedybooks.com

Activity books ~ Colouring books ~ Dot to dot ~ Reading books ~ Grammar books
Workbooks ~ Word search puzzles ~ Notebooks ~ Journals and Sketchbooks

Printed in Great Britain
by Amazon

84334640R00025